Anaiah Dupont-Spencer is a young caregiver who has always had a passion for creative writing and mental health from an early age. She has merged her personal life and work experiences within her novels, to create books that open up conversation about taboo topics. Anaiah has been writing from age 12 onwards, from novels to poetry, and is studying forensic psychology. Through juggling a degree and full-time employment for the NHS, she still makes time to fulfil her writing and creative desires.

This book is dedicated to all those who have, and still are, suffering from mental health or traumatic experiences. I want this book to not only empower those who feel defeated, but to also educate those who may have a lack of understanding or hold any judgement or prejudice. This caters to those who are young, old, male, and female as trauma and mental health doesn't discriminate.

Anaiah Dupont-Spencer

THINGS ONLY GET
WORSE TO GET BETTER

AUSTIN MACAULEY PUBLISHERS™

LONDON • CAMBRIDGE • NEW YORK • SHARJAH

A CIP catalogue record for this title is available from the British Library.

ISBN 9781398426177 (Paperback)
ISBN 9781398426184 (ePub e-book)

www.austinmacauley.com

First Published 2022
Austin Macauley Publishers Ltd®
1 Canada Square
Canary Wharf
London
E14 5AA

I would like to thank Austin Macauley Publishers for considering my book and for giving me the opportunity as a new author to share my work.

Chapter 1

Depression

Depression – feeling of severe despondency and dejection.

It creeps up on you unexpectedly. It appears any time of the day and any time of the night. It steals any thought of content from you when you need it most. It has no care or regard for you. It wants to see you belittled, broken and beaten down. The smile on your face and glow in your eyes slowly but surely turns to tears. You feel empty inside, you feel worthless. Why do I feel like this? What did I do? You existed that's what. You breathe in this everyday air. Your heart beats. Your lungs expand. That's the problem. It tells you what a waste of life you are, how unwanted you are, how useless you are and that all you deserve is nothing but dismay and torment.

You try to shut it out but you can only do so for so long. Once you finally crack a smile and raise your head high, it comes back and knocks you down harder and harder each time. You try to pick yourself back up with words like "It'll be okay", "You'll be all right" and then it pushes you back down. Reminding you that "You're a worthless piece of shit", "You're a mess, look at you"; that empty feeling in your stomach comes back, that stabbing feeling in your chest becomes sharper. You want to scream that you're okay but all you can do is cry out that you're not. You're not okay. You're hurt. Broken. Empty. You feel nothing but despair.

You drag your lifeless body through the day, pretending to be a ball of positivity when you're just a body without a soul, existing in this cruel, cold world. You feel alone but you don't know why. You have friends and family but you don't feel a part of any social group. You have a job but you don't feel validated or important. You have a partner but you don't feel loved. You have a heart but it has just given up. You can't feel what is not there. You can't experience what you won't have. You can't try what's not worth it. So you ponder in a deep sea of your thoughts and slowly drown yourself in the constant whirlpool of dismay and self-rejection.

It comes and goes so often that it's become a part of who you are, what you are and how you are as an individual. It's become a characteristic of yours. It belongs to you yet it owns you. It is your master and you its slave. You are a degenerate to your own thoughts and feelings. If it tells you, you are nothing then you accept that as your fate. This then becomes a toxic cycle. You expect it to come back. You wait for it to come back. Then eventually you want it to come back because it is the only thing that is consistent in your life. Depression is the only thing you have that you know will not walk out on you. It will not leave you. It will always come back to remind you who you are. If it doesn't then who will?

Contentment

Contentment – a state of happiness and satisfaction.

It's okay to feel shitty – in fact, it's perfectly normal. There are plenty of ways to cheer yourself up – chocolate, movies and friends. However when you're experiencing depression these things are utterly useless. Depression makes you feel like there's no escape, there's no way out and that no one can help. But there is always a solution to any problem. You can't cure depression instantly, and like anything it is a process. You can't pray depression away like many religious folks tell you to. "God will make it better" or "You're not really depressed". Words like these should be shut out and ignored. A holy saviour may give some hope but for others it's a reminder of rejection for a being they cannot see and haven't endured. When people try to tell you what you are feeling is not real, it creates self-hate and confusion as to why you feel the way you do. You blame yourself for these feelings when the actual culprit is only a clinical diagnosis away.

Talking, some say is the best start. Speaking about how you feel, and opening up can be very difficult but it's the beginning of your journey. You can share how you feel inside, and finally not bottle up your feelings. Talking is one step away from depression and one step towards satisfaction. Phone helplines and talking to general physicians can make you feel patronised, less masculine if you're male and even weak. Medication can create fear of losing yourself completely, and can stir up worry about what other people may think of you. "They must be mad", "They belong in an institution", when in reality fuck what they all think. People project negativity on those who they envy or feel threatened by. They do this in order to validate themselves and give themselves a feeling of non-existent superiority. People hurt others to repair themselves. The world we live in is selfish.

Put yourself first. Every breath you take is worth it. You are worth it. Everything you do is worth it. Be the best version of yourself and don't you dare let depression bring you down. Prove it wrong; show it you are no longer under its jurisdiction. Break down all the barriers it created for you. Ignore all the names it called you. Kick over the feelings of isolation and rejection it subjected you to. Talk to someone. Go on medication. Engage in counselling. Do anything you must do to break away from this abusive relationship.

That's what depression is; an unhealthy, vicious domestic abuse type of ownership. The emotional abuse you experience is not going to be dominant in your life forever. Walk away and don't look back. Leave it behind, you are worth more. You are unique. Tell this to yourself every morning. I'm funny. I'm smart. I'm gorgeous/handsome. I am a bad ass human-fucking-being. You tell depression to go find another bitch because you are moving on to something so much better. You are going to begin dating contentment.

Contentment makes you smile, makes you feel warm inside. Contentment brings you joy and happiness. It lets you experience the good things. You roll over in bed and wake to contentment and you actually feel good for once. It makes you feel appreciated, gives you more confidence, and just makes you feel okay. Contentment may take a while to come along and sometimes it will leave you. You just have to remember the steps you took to meet contentment and know it is always there, you just need to find the mentality to access it. Once you have contentment in your life, it is yours to keep.

Chapter 2
Anxiety

Anxiety – a feeling of worry, nervousness and unease. Constant distress and constant fear. Constant worry and concern about what's to come and what may or may not happen. It makes you shake while your legs begin jittering and your feet pat in distress up and down against the floor. You don't know what to do or how to act; you're just flooded with thoughts that are contagious with feeling vulnerable. You think everyone's looking at you; it makes you feel like everyone is only looking at you. Hundreds of eyes glaring, wondering what's wrong. Your heart pounds and you become breathless. It's like you're being chased by somewhat of a beast when in reality you're just walking down the aisle of the bus looking for a seat before it begins to move.

It makes you feel as if you have to reinforce what is normal. You're walking through the market and anxious that you're being watched; that people are trying to figure you out so you must pretend to be what they expect you to be. An ordinary person. You pretend to be on the phone and even that increases your anxiety as you wonder whether someone has deciphered your poor attempt of looking casual. You and your thoughts argue back and forth in your head as you try to compromise and tell them it's going to be okay; but they keep arguing back telling you that you are the odd one out.

You try to keep on going but you can't. You try to ignore it but you can't. Your hands are shaking constantly, your head is down to the ground so you can't see the environment that places you under such threat. But it just doesn't work. Your body is filled with constant unease and you feel scared but you don't know what is it that scares you. You walk off to a secluded place, thrust your head against the wall and let out a cry. "Why can't I be normal?" Your body slumps down against the wall and you feel like you can't breathe. You become more and more nervous. More and more distressed. All of this triggered just from trying to get home. A simple task to some while complex one to others.

The simplest tasks feel impossible when you experience this complex lexis. That is anxiety. The nasty culprit who makes saying hello feel like swallowing bleach. It makes walking home feel like walking through an active battle field. You can't go anywhere without your heart racing through the roof. You can't eat anything in front of people without the fear of choking or the thought of what someone thinks about the way you eat. You can't sit with friends as your social awkwardness comes to light and reminds people why you lack friends. That is the occupation of anxiety, to make you feel afraid of the world and what's to come. You're consumed by fear. Yet anxiety seems to be the only thing protecting you from rejection and further sorrow.

Calmness

Calmness – the state or quality of being free from agitation or strong emotion.

Breathing helps. Deep breaths. Nice and slow. This helps bring about feelings of tranquillity and peace. The anxious feelings can slowly fade away as long as you focus on not what you're feeling but on how to minimise feeling that way. You need to consciously and subconsciously tell yourself it's going to be okay. No one is judging you; they have better things to do. You don't need to pretend and you don't need to impress. Adopt the mind-set of not caring about other's opinions. This will takes steps of erasing the constant self-rejection and self-consciousness associated with anxiety.

I've always felt less anxious when I put in my headphones and burst the music to top volume. This way I can shut the outside world out and not concentrate on what other people are doing. Your mind can focus on what's important and that's reaching your destination without having a breakdown. Walking through the town centre once felt and occasionally still does feel impossible, but caring less about the subjective conversations on matters of opinion helped me jump that milestone. One small step for me, and one big step for all of those bullied by anxiety.

I'm not going to tell you that you won't ever feel anxious. It's perfectly normal, especially in unambiguous situations. However once you find calmness, it will walk you through these situations and it will feel effortless. Calmness is that sweet mother soothing her child. Calmness tells you everything will be okay as it holds your hands and supports you throughout your struggles. Calmness helps slow your breathing and gets your emotions in check, that feeling of comfort will help you to relax and continue your journey at ease. Calmness will shield those bad thoughts, calmness will grasp your hand and stop the shaking further it will rest its hand on your shaking legs and soothe you. Calmness is that one thing you will always find within yourself. It is yours to keep for as long as you allow it access to you.

Chapter 3
Body Dysmorphia

Body dysmorphia – being preoccupied by an imagined physical defect or minor defect that often others cannot see. Skinny. Fat. Ugly. Unattractive. That's what you believe you are. The mirror is only a constant reminder of how you're not good enough. You'll never be loved. You'll never be pursued. You'll never be perceived as beautiful. You're not enough. Social media reinforces this – what you should be, and yet something that you'll never be. Perfect exists, but perfect is not a word that would be used to describe you. Your waist isn't slim enough. Your bust isn't big enough. Your hips don't go out like this. Your thigh gap isn't wide enough. You're too tall. You're too short. You're too overweight. You don't weigh enough. Your skin is too light. Your skin is too dark. Your hair isn't long enough. Your hair isn't thick enough. Nothing about you is enough.

You wake up every morning, thinking of new ways to attempt to alter yourself. "If I eat this many bars of chocolate will it go to my bum?" You follow that routine and it creates another problem. Now you've put on a few too many pounds. "I look fat don't I?" That voice in your head will never do anything but bring you down. It'll tell you that you appear to look in ways that you don't. "You're a bit on the plump side." Even though you're only 110 pounds. You're this. You're that. The constant judgement soon gets to you as much as you try to ignore it, especially as soon as you notice people beginning to agree with that voice in your head. An additional reminder of what you lack.

Now you're gagging yourself after every meal in hope that those extra calories will no longer count. Now you're starving yourself to lose a few pounds that have now turned to a few stone. Or now you're crying about your weight that you were once comfortable with, as your new weight no longer fits society's expectations. Being slim is no longer a trend. Being plus size was never a trend. Being "thick" becomes looking fake or plastic. Nothing is good enough. Now you're too slim. Now you're too curvy. Now your lips are too big. Your hair is too long. You're too tanned. Now you're too much. You were once less. Now you're too much. And yet still not enough.

Your reflection in the mirror begins to fade into the pool of tears filling your eyes. You can no longer see yourself. You don't recognise who you are. You picked yourself apart and now you can't find the pieces to put yourself back together. Your body dysmorphia has destroyed you. Yet you keep telling yourself, it only wants you to become the best version you can be. It only wants you to be objectified and perceived as beautiful. It only wants the best for you, right?

Self-love

Self-love – regard for one's own well-being and happiness.

Perfect, beautiful and amazing. That's what you are. Telling yourself these things won't make you cocky or big headed, in actual fact they reflect the self-appreciation and confidence you deserve to own. Don't let the evil thoughts of body dysmorphia or people in general tell you what you need to be. Don't let it talk you down. Don't let it make you feel like you're worthless or your value is minimal. Do you know why? It's because you are WORTH so much more than that. You don't have to feel it, you just have to know it. Look in the mirror and smile. Don't pick things out you don't like about yourself rather pick things you do like. I'm smart. I'm confident. I don't let people bring me down. I don't let it bring me down. Turn down all of that negative energy and don't attempt to disguise it as constructive criticism. That's hatred, a form of manipulation to bring you down not better you.

Looks are subjective. There'll always be that one person, one who thinks that you're the best thing that ever happened to them. But do not rely on another being to make you feel validated or appreciated. You didn't come into this world to be told how attractive you are or how this asset of yours is societally measured. You came into this world to live your life the way you want and how you want; without the consistent breakdowns and tear filled nights of not feeling good enough. Love yourself is all I can say. There's no love more powerful than self-love. If someone name calls you it's because they are projecting their own unhappiness unto you-another form of self-hate; so do not retaliate and either ignore them or show them your journey of self-love.

This phrase is corny but "don't hate, appreciate". Don't hate yourself, appreciate yourself. Yes, we all have things we want to change about ourselves. Yes, we all want to have aspects of another person. Yet self-hate and jealousy is not the solution. Accept who you are and then you can love who you are. If you truly love yourself, who can take that away? Nobody. Not even dysmorphia. It's like learning that the sky is blue and grass is green. Once you learn this, you never forget it. Someone can keep telling you that the sky is pink and the grass is yellow, but you know it's not so you don't take that observation into account. Do that in regards to loving yourself. If you know your worth then no one can tell you otherwise.

Chapter 4

Self-Harm

Self-harm – deliberate injury to oneself. You did it once; "Just this one time," you said. You did it the second time, "I won't do it again," you said. Eventually the excuses pile up and eventually the open wounds spread like wild fire. Each scar with its own story to tell. The first was to see how it feels – empowering. You have control. You watch the blood pour as you slice and dice your arms as if preparing raw meat. It hurts at first. But the pain soon turns to relief. Then to tears and regret. That wound is always an open reminder of your downfall. Yet you're tempted to do it again. You're the one who gets to decide to hurt yourself, and when you hurt yourself – it's not like before when you didn't expect to be hurt. When you were vulnerable, another being's victim. Now you are your own victim, you decide it all. How. When. What. And why. It started as a cry for help, and then turned into a way out of living. It never worked, no matter how deep you cut. There's no other way to make the pain inside hurt less; so you rip yourself apart on the outside and see if it makes a difference. Will the suffering stop? Will the rejection go away? But all that fades is your soul. It drifts away, after each cut. You start to feel less alive, you start to feel and care less. You're just a piece of road-kill. You're mangled and disfigured. You don't feel any better. But it's telling you to do it again. You have no reason not to. It's just flesh. Flesh that no one cares about, whether it is dead or alive. Turn it into an art displaying all your sorrows. Reveal how broken you are to the world. Let them know that they broke you, and the glass is what left the cuts – the scars are the evidence. Ten scars equal to ten stories. Each cut precise, each cut brimming to tell a tale. You want to resist but the pain becomes somewhat satisfying. Laughter mixed with tears to cover up the hurt you're experiencing. Someone hurt you. You might as well hurt yourself. All you are is a punching bag. That voice in your head won't go away. It tells you to keep going. One more. Two more. Let's go for fifteen more. You run out of appropriate clothes to cover the marks. You eventually give up caring and let people see. You shrug it off and say you're okay. "I fell", "It was an accident", then the excuses give up on themselves too. "I cut myself. And I like it"; the shock and horror on people's face is always a picture. They don't know how to react, and yet it is people like them who day after day assist the reality of self-harm. Bullies, rapists, and abusers. You don't have to hold the knife; your actions already cut out my heart, and passed the blade to my lifeless hands and helped me slit my wrists.

People always assume self-harm is some sick illness or pain fetish. It's far from that. It's an escape. It's an attempt to experience relief, to feel alive, and to fill the void of emptiness inside. If I feel pain, I feel something. You need to feel something, whether it's good or bad. Self-harm is never a pretty sight. Neither is the process that leads to self-harm. it's as if you're watching a flower blossom and over time it starts to wilt. You don't cut your body for attention. You cut your body for a solution. Yet get addicted and can't stop. The only permanent friends you have are your scars. They're yours to keep. You own them. Not the bullies, rapists, or abusers. They're reminders that you have all collectively stolen my soul, pushed me to my knees. And forced me to beg to God for forgiveness for actions that were not my own. No means yes and yes means cut. I slit my wrists because I am not enough.

Self-Preservation

Self-preservation – the protection of oneself from harm.

Not harming yourself isn't as simple as locking away anything and everything sharp. To move away from this habit, you need to delve deep into why it started. What caused you to hurt yourself? What can you do to not see self-harm as an escape? Two very big questions. You need to love your body in order not to dismantle it. Each scar may tell a story but each scar is a symbol that your foe has won. You've allowed it or them to break you down to the point where you not only have experienced damage from others, but you now experience it from yourself. You have become your own torturer. You interrogate yourself for things you yet do not understand. Why does this happen to me? Why won't it stop? What did I do? You can't answer these questions so you turn to the blade. Instead of pouring your heart out and expressing how you feel, you pour blood out of your veins to express what you feel you can't talk about. Yes you may feel some relief, but that relief is temporary. You reach an optimum high and when you get back down, the pain hits even harder. No matter how many times you cut, it will never be enough and yes that may reflect how you feel momentarily but what would you prefer – an endless cycle of hurt and upset or a way out? I'm telling you from the depth of my heart; it is not worth it because you hold value. You are someone special and you may not think it, but you are special to someone. If you can protect yourself from yourself you can protect yourself from others. Guard your heart but be open to kindness and to help especially. Your body is a temple, don't break your own walls down.

Sometimes I wake and look at my own scars. They used to be a reminder of how hopeless life used to be, but now they're a milestone of how far I've come. Now it's your turn. Take a step away from mutilation and a jump towards healing. I can't tell you how to do it because everyone is different. Just let this be a reminder that self-harm isn't the only way to feel "better". Confront what made you feel this way, push out the negative thoughts. Ignore that voice in your head telling you to pick up a razor. You tell it you know your worth, you're better than that. Your body isn't a piece of wood to carve into, rather it's an art to be praised. Appreciated, loved and respected.

You may feel like you're constantly hurting but does a zebra walk into a lion's den or does it run to safety? Don't fraternise with your demons, summon them to hell and walk on by to paradisc.

Chapter 5

Anger

Anger – a strong feeling of annoyance, displeasure or hostility.

You can't control it. You don't know why you feel this way. All you know is that you can't contain it. It's driving you mad. The feeling of despair and despondency has developed to a feeling of rage. You want to calm down but you can't. You start to react, throw things. Scream. Shout. Lay hands on anyone in the way. Yet there's still that timid voice in your head, screaming to be heard. Telling you to take a deep breath and stay calm. You try to listen to it, you want to listen to it but there's something blocking your body from reciprocating your thoughts. All you can do is rage until there's nothing left to rage about. You're uncontrollable. You can't be tamed. You maul everyone and everything around you; and one day you'll discover there's nothing or anyone left.

The littlest things trigger you nowadays. All that pain and hurt that you felt before and dealt with in silence is no longer an available option. You want to keep quiet and act rationally, but the constant disrespect and disregard you've endured is uncontainable and you only know one way to act.

Flip out. Kick off. Show them all you're not one to be pushed about. Maybe people will back off then? Maybe then people may not say the things they say or do the things they do? Or maybe I should stay calm. Everything's building up and you can't take it anymore. You've been beat down with words and actions. Now you've grasped onto the pain, lifted yourself up by the hanging pity and have filled yourself with so much hostility that everything around you drops like dead bodies.

After you've let it all out, you still feel the same. You've not achieved anything nor benefited. Things are the exact as they were before. In fact they are actually even worse. Maybe that's why you get pissed-off. If being timid and weak did nothing; then maybe turning into an unfiltered, with no limits, no boundaries, and no regard for others type of person; then maybe just maybe you'd feel slightly more content. Less hurt. But no, you feel worst. That emptiness remains and that temper remains. That lifeless soul of yours remains. You hurt others in an attempt to fix what's broken about yourself. One man's weakness is another man's newly found strength. That's what you thought at least. But instead it's your downfall. It's a side to you that only the devil himself lusts after. When you flip the switch, your inner demon manifests through your tongue and the words it spits are poison to the body, mind and soul.

Pleasantness

Pleasantness – the quality of being enjoyable.

It makes you feel at ease. Calm and relaxed. It robs all discontent and replaces it with a sense of likability. It makes you feel better about yourself as you feel more in control. You are able to enjoy and find comfort in your emotions and direct them anywhere you please. Your burst of anger begins to shrink gradually; your explosions of content begin to grow rapidly. As you start to feel better about the way you feel; the people around you start to feel better when in your presence. You're no longer a ticking time bomb that everyone expects to go off; you are a butterfly learning to fly, learning to be gracious and delightful. Your mannerisms have left behind thoughts of anger and have begun to journey to discover new linguistics with ambitions to become better and improved.

This section isn't to tell you that you can't get angry, it's to display that there is another side to you when you need to ease the compilation of anger. Don't suppress the urges, address them appropriately, calmly and respectfully. Eventually that constant arguing in your head about what to do will become comical to you. You'll be able to tell anger to stand down and reassess the circumstances. Once you do that you'll be able to make yourself become at ease. Yet simultaneously don't let anybody treat you like their puppet, handle your anger with class. Silence is the biggest instigator to a bully who craves altercations and lives off the suffering of another's downfall.

When you fall down and crash to the floor, grab the hand of pleasantness, who'll look down and appreciate its new acquaintance. It will make your heart beat slow down and normalise its pace; it will make you feel warm inside and it will congratulate you on your new alliance. Ignore the scolding hand of anger. All he wants is to stop you feeling things that it can't itself. It feels down so it wants to synchronise its short temper with you. All it does is manipulate your feelings and flip the switch to the lights of solutions that are a way out of this emotion. You can no longer find your other options; as anger has blinded you and shut out any compromise. Anger wants your head to pound, your heart to race and your fists to clench and massacre any trace of rationality.

Once you experience that feeling of pleasantness, you will always know it's there with your best interest at heart. Pleasantness will cuddle you whilst you're sleeping, comfort you whilst you are awake and skip through your troubles with you hand in hand. Pleasantness is something so beautiful that its gaze is one you will never forget and the thought of anger will become a concept of sloppy seconds. You've had anger and you're no longer feeling it anymore. You've lost your attraction to it. You've found something way better, i.e. pleasantness. Pleasantness will put a ring on your finger and vow to cherish you; whereas anger is here to take you for all you own. Pleasantness is the contraception against the impure thoughts of anger.

Chapter 6

Post-Traumatic Stress
Disorder (PTSD)

PTSD – an anxiety disorder caused by very stressful, frightening or distressing events.

Okay one minute. An insecure mess the next. You can never predict when the flashbacks will be retrieved. When your brain gives you an inconvenient reminder of all the trauma that you've been through. All the things you don't want to remember come flooding back in a split second; knocking you to the ground and drowning you in its wave of despair. You become susceptible to your past experiences. You want to forget but it won't let you. It's back to haunt you. Break you down. Drag you back to what was once your reality. The fatality and pain consumes your mind, and reminds you that what was once taken from you can be taken again and again, until you become enslaved to it. It thrives off the process of forcing you to turn that disbelief into acceptance.

It wants to inflict pain on you. It wants you to remember it. It severs your grasping hands holding onto the prospect of moving on. It pushes you away from recovery. It steals any new-found happiness and replaces it, with that one unforgettable moment that continues to replay in your mind. You want to forget what had happened. You want to break free from the chains holding you down; preventing you from escaping from that day. You've experienced freedom and choice and now you never want to let go of that. Yet it keeps coming back. It's lurking and watching. Then pounces when you're at your weakest – when you actually feel okay. It kidnaps your happiness and no matter how fast you run to take it back, you fall behind.

You fall back into that hole where you've become trapped. Every time you pull yourself up; there surfaces a memory of when your knickers were viciously torn. Or when your lover beat you black and blue. Or when you watched comrades be shot lifeless. It comes back to remind you of the strength you didn't have and it eventually starts to make you go mad. Any similar sound, noise, smell or voice can be a trigger for the trauma. A reminder. You slump against the wall and all you can do is scream. Shout and cry. Words come out but they don't make sense. You can't comprehend how you feel right now or how to stop it. Your head is ringing, all the thoughts rushing at once. You hit yourself on the side of your head repeatedly; begging for it to stop. But you can't. It stops once it's drenched you in fear. It won't let you forget. Not one second of it. PTSD is your dealer. No matter how many times it gets locked up and put away in a cell; it always come back to sell you more bad memories whether you're buying or not.

Progression

Progression – moving gradually towards a more advanced state.

The memories will always be there, but they've become subdued. You won't forget but you can forgive, if not move forward. That flickering pain becomes a feeling of achievement; you survived, you bounced back and you're still here. The pity and sorrow you feel for yourself begins to fade and you become stronger. You took your past and used its broken pieces to build something more stable. PTSD is an old friend who you no longer associate with. It can't affect you how it did before, because you won't let it. You have met progression who is there to support you through those hard times when PTSD attempts to return. Progression will stand up for you and turn PTSD away. Progression is your protector and the reason why PTSD can't knock you down. It's harder to fall when you have a hand to hold onto.

You'll have your down days; you'll have the occasional flashback and reminder. But ever since progression came into your life, those thoughts will never affect you like they did before. You feel empowered by your experience not victimised. What happened was aimed to put you down but now you've got back up and are speaking out. Bad things happen. When they do happen, you have two choices. You use it to make a difference or you allow yourself to become a victim. You allow them to win. You used to but not anymore. Once wilted and now watered back to life, you have blossomed. You've become an inspiration for others to speak up.

No hate in your heart will prevent you from backtracking because progression is here to make you feel whole.

Progression is here to help you move forward. Progression is here to support you when no one else did. Progression isn't a replacement for forgetting. Progression is there to show you the bigger picture and to help you move beyond your past – it doesn't want those things to define you. You are who you choose to become and not what something made you. You are not the one to take accountability of the actions of others but you are accountable for how you choose to carry yourself. A baby bird that has fallen from its nest does not sit there and accept its circumstance, it cries out for its mother and tries to fly to safety. Don't mope around in self-pity and sorrow rather fight back for what was taken from you and make a difference. Progression comes along to help you in this. Progression is here to save you from the raging fire aroused by PTSD. You must accept in order to progress.

Chapter 7

Loneliness

Loneliness – sadness due to one having a lack of or no company.

Empty. The only word that can describe how you feel. You have nothing nor no one, and now you've forgotten how it is to feel. To feel emotions and to feel empathy because you've forgotten how to do so. You've not experienced the company of others for so long, you don't know how to express emotiveness as you've had no one to express it to. You don't get mad because there's no one to make you angry and you don't cry either because there's no one to hurt you. This sounds more peaceful and stress-free, but then you remember you don't smile because there's no one to make you happy. That feeling of emptiness inside arises and digs deep into your stomach making you want to cry out. You feel alone so you walk alone like a young wolf cub abandoned by its pack. Loneliness has created a hole inside you that's gradually compacting itself with sorrow, pity and pain.

You push people away yet at the same time attempt to grasp onto them, but that empty feeling in your heart cannot hold on for any longer, your fingers slip and you finally let go. You attract what you project. All you know how to project is a negative atmosphere. You don't mean to, it's accidental. You only express how you feel and that's nothing. People don't understand, in fact people don't care. It becomes a "you problem", you can't share what's on your mind because it makes people uncomfortable. You can't share what's happened to you because it makes people pity you.

You're a person with baggage and no one is ready to carry it. So again you procrastinate on the things you can't keep – family, friends, colleagues and partners. No one is there for you but you, yourself. You want someone to lean on but they take their shoulder, move away and let you hit the ground. Loneliness creeps back, strokes your face and reminds you, it is all you have. Your routine is the same. You wake and fall asleep alone. You speak to no one. You socialise with no one. You sit on the edge of the bed fantasising about what it'd be like to have people surrounding you, then loneliness makes a visit and sets you straight. It again reminds you about everything wrong with you. You're weird. You don't fit in. You're not good enough. You're not attractive enough. You're not fun enough. You just aren't a "people person". Eventually you tell yourself that it is okay to be alone, who needs friends anyway? But then that burning sensation tingles throughout your body, your eyes tear up and all you can do is cry.

You don't know what to do, how to change what you're feeling and all loneliness can do is try to justify it. It wraps its hands around your throat, till your face turns blue and tells you the suffocation you're experiencing, not being able to breathe is exactly what company will do to you. People will use your body till it becomes lifeless. Till you're no longer of any use. We live in a world of take, not give. Once everything's taken from you, you'll have nothing left to exchange. Once you lack this, you're no longer of any further value. Loneliness will protect you from the wrath of humanity. Like I said you can't get hurt, if there's no one around to hurt you. So you become content with being isolated and that's okay because loneliness knows what's best for you. Loneliness is your protector from predators; loneliness is your lover who takes care of you. Loneliness will be the God watching over you. However, it is also the devil waiting for its opportunity to send you in to a whirlpool of madness.

Inclusion

Inclusion – being included within a group or a social structure.

People should never be your top priority; you should always put yourself first. However, the company of others offers a cushion of comfort and support when required. You don't necessarily have to open up but being open to allowing people into your life is important. As much as we all want to be independent and not rely on anyone, we lack basic understanding of morals as there is no one to remind us of them. This creates a cycle of lack of emotion. You forget how to feel, how to love, and how to want/desire because there's no one along to experience it with you. Inclusion is here to make you feel included – you know that there is always someone there. Someone to cry to and someone to vent to, when one desires to do so. These things help keep us sane and prevent us bottling things up. If you screw the lid to your open heart tight enough and it gets shaken, it'll explode.

Inclusion wants to introduce you to your peers to remind you that not everyone is the same. Inclusion leaves good morning messages on your phone. It asks you about your day and offers to take you out. Inclusion cheers you up when you're at your lowest; it's your shoulder to cry on. It's everything you need to balance your emotions before they tumble off the edge and cause you serious damage. Inclusion surrounds you with positivity and people and ensures that you're never truly alone. Yes sometimes inclusion will annoy you, give you relationship drama and cause you to fall out with your friends but these are all normal aspects of life. Things that are meant to be experienced and are life lessons that are meant to be learned.

Inclusion will give you itself, a book and tell you to read up on it. It wants you to feed on its knowledge because knowledge is power and with power you are unstoppable. The wiser you get, the more magnetic you become. The energy you give out is the energy you attract and all inclusion wants to do is guide you. It wants to help you break out of your cocoon, spread your wings and glide through the sky to show the world your inner beauty. With inclusion, your loneliness disappears. Loneliness has lost its purpose, packed its bags and hopped on to the train – destination, another vulnerable soul.

Inclusion gives you company while loneliness gives you isolation and seclusion. Inclusion makes you feel confident and loneliness makes you feel worthless. Inclusion shows you, you are special and loneliness shows you, you are not.

Would you rather be cherished and appreciated or live with self-pity and keep on feeling down? Would you rather have a hand to hold, to lift you up or would you prefer one that pushes you back to the ground? Inclusion will give you access to happiness whereas loneliness just wants to see you disintegrate into a puddle of dismay that people walk around to avoid dampening their mood.

Chapter 8

Bipolar

Bipolar – manic or depressive episodes.

Happy today and feeling like shit tomorrow. Smiling for now, quickly replaced by a frown. Angry this second while crying out in the next. That's life for you – a canine of uncontrollable thoughts and feelings that's been let off the leash, and no matter how fast you run after your old life, you can't catch up to it. Bipolar is the extremity of mood swings. It forces your mood to change almost instantly. You wake up in the morning, feeling great and then those unclean thoughts fester into your mind sickening you to the pit of your stomach. No matter how hard happiness fights back, sadness, hurt and pain suppress it without having to lift a single finger. Now here you are again in bed, unaware of what's caused you to suddenly feel this way; but all you know is that's how you're feeling: unappreciated, worthless and empty.

It begins to drive you mad. You hit yourself again and again on your head while attempting to knock out those thoughts. You punch the wall. Kick, smash and break anything. You scream that you need help and want it to stop. You fall to the ground and let the wave of tears break free.

You can't breathe. Your chest is tight and you are panting. Gasping for breath. Your head rises a bit and you look around; all you can do is manically laugh. You're giggling and smiling. You don't know what's funny but you're all cheery now. Your tears are dried up and you have the biggest grin on your face. Bipolar has just stuck a blade in your chest to watch you die but then changed its mind. Bipolar has performed first aid to bring you back to life.

These episodes are constant; they come out of the blue. You don't know why or how they happen. You can't explain why you're suddenly angry or feeling upset but that's what it does; throws your emotions into the washing machine without separating the colours and now everything's stained. Happiness has mixed with sadness. Anger has mixed with pain. Now you can no longer wear one emotion at once; as bipolar causes you to constantly switch between all these feelings. It is driving you crazy; it's making you distance yourself away from people. You don't want anyone to set eyes on your manic vulnerability. What would they think? You're crazy and out of control. You don't want to believe it and you feel like you can control it when you know deep down that you simply can't.

No matter how hard you try bipolar keeps on taking what you want to experience and giving you what makes you want to experience nothing at all. Sometimes you want to leave the reality that you're condemned to face. You can't find peace, not even from sleeping because the thoughts battle amongst each other. All you can hear are the war cries and bodies dropping one by one. That's how you feel as you keep losing control to choose each emotion that you feel one by one. You hide away from people, so they can't witness your 20 different sides. You hide away from light so that you don't have to look at yourself. You start to remember that you can't actually hide yourself from anything; because who you truly are is gone.

Anger, loneliness, depression, contentment and pleasantness have all taken you hostage. Each emotion takes on the role of being you. They switch roles as often as you blink. It's almost a high as you feel too much at once. You're still somewhere inside, deep down but your head's being pushed down further under the water; soon it'll be so deep that resuscitation will be out of the question. Bipolar won't allow you to experience anything for too long, each emotion must remain savoured. What's the fun in one at a time, when you can have it all?

Comfort

Comfort – to ease grief or trouble of something in particular.

Comfort is something special. It's a pillow to fall back on and it makes you feel safe. It's there to make you feel at ease; to experience calmness and allows you to place your worries into a box labelled "not required until further notice". You can roll over and look comfort in the eye and know it'll never leave you. Once you feel comforted over something, you will continue to feel that way forever. Comfort is that support to help you move away from all your worries and fears. It's the pickup truck taking all the things you need and leaving what you don't behind.

Bipolar wants to bring all your baggage but comfort is here to deny it. Not anymore. It doesn't get to dictate how you feel. If you want to be happy then you must allow yourself to experience it for as long as you please, not until bipolar says so. Whether it's breathing techniques, yoga or medication you need to tell bipolar where the door is and then do it. Comfort is here to walk you through the next stages of your life; without the constant anxiety of all your emotions trying to trip you up all at once. Comfort is the trampoline that'll boost you up when you come back down. Each time you fall down, you bounce back up higher. High enough to be out of negativity's grasp. Comfort is who you turn to when you're feeling lost and don't know what to do or how to get better. It's there to tell you everything's going to be all right. It wants you to see the positive aspects of life as there's so much more you can do, see and learn. Don't let bipolar prevent you from becoming more than what you are. Comfort can't do everything for you but it's there to remind you and you have it to make you feel okay.

A plaster is comfort to a paper cut. A bosom is comfort to a hungry babe. To feel at ease is your comfort to bipolar, to feel one thing at a time and to control your emotions. Take charge of who you are, are just some of the many forms of comfort you are able to purchase. The only price you have to pay is actively pushing yourself to make a change. Not for anybody else but for yourself.

Don't feel pitiful for having to say that you need help or support. Feel empowered as you are taking action to take steps towards recovery and steps away from what is persecution and pain that bipolar subjects you to. The biggest step is admitting that something isn't right. Once you've done that the rest is not so hard. Say goodbye to bipolar and begin to hang out with comfort. Comfort wants you to become the best version of yourself that you can be. Take into account what friend wants to see you become successful, and what friend is in secret competition with you.

Chapter 9

Rape

Rape – when one or multiple individuals force another into non-consensual sexual acts.

You are stripped of your dignity, your self-respect and your clothes. Your mind, body and soul repeatedly raped, beaten and mutilated. Frozen like ice. You can't move or speak. All you can do is shed a tear, turn your head to the side and pray for it to be over. The sound of him grunting rings in your ears, deafening you. His sweat dripping onto your chest; burning through your skin like acid. His grasp around your neck suffocates you. You want to fall unconscious so that you can forget. But he holds your head, so that you have to face him. He looks you in the eye and grins.

Rape is here to take you for all it can and leave you with nothing. Rape will rip your genitals, leave its mark and scar not only on your body but also your mind. The aftermath affects you physically and mentally. It won't leave, rape is here to stay and keep you frail, weak and vulnerable. Rape has forcibly spread your legs and spat on such a delicacy. This delicacy has now become accessible to any man who cannot compensate for his lack of masculinity and cannot understand the word no. Rape has pinned you down, pulled up your dress and reminded you, that you are not the owner of the goods in-between your legs. You're only the holder of goods who distributes as and when you're told.

Once your body has drained its uninvited guest, all you can do is lie still. You reminisce and blame yourself. You wore too much makeup or were your clothes too tight? You're to blame. Rape would've skipped on by? Wouldn't it? Rape only preys on the weak and you probably made it easy. You didn't fight back hard enough. You didn't scream loud enough. All you did was giving up quickly. You accepted your situation and lied lifelessly. Your hands crushed into the ground. Legs spread so far apart that your bones cracked. You are left in a pool of your blood and rape's semen.

Rape came along while you played hide and seek; it found you. Now you suffer the consequences of a life combined with a lack of trust and fear of men. You can no longer give up what was taken from you. You can no longer enjoy the act that caused such hurt. You can no longer love that act because this act was previously tinged with violence. You're not a woman. You're a mere property. They can go in and out of you without knocking. Choice is non-existent, ownership is patriarchal and acceptance is your only option.

You stumble to your feet. Your body in such agony, you cannot keep balance for long. Thrown around like a rag doll, stamped on like an insect. Hit and run. You're left for dead. Spat on, violated, assaulted and the word people like to put aside – raped. Your free will, stolen. Your choice, limited. Your protest and denial, ignored. Only the sickest can take pleasure from a woman's cries. But there's nothing you can do. It has happened. Now move on. Until rape comes back again and fucks/sucks the last bit of sanity out of you. That's what happens. You don't experience sex, rather, you experienced a loss; a loss of safety, enjoyment, happiness, and trust. You lost everything you once had and rebuilding that feels almost impossible. Rape gives the predator power and the victim susceptibility. Slowly, but surely, you become dead inside. That beautiful butterfly has lost its wings, fallen to the ground and rotten into the soil.

There's nothing left. Your soul blackened and your mind poisoned. Your body is out of bounds. You've grown thorns, so no one can touch. You've become bitter so no one converses with you. You've become less attractive so no one looks your way. Rape won't desire you, right? You're wrong yet again. It lurks around every dark corner, in every bush and could be disguised as a stranger, friend, family member or even your lover. Rape takes on any form, size, and persona; rape has absolutely no preference. You will always be a potential to rape and there's nothing you can do. Rape stalks you in the night and day. Rape watches you at work and social gatherings. Rape can even raise you as a small child. Rape's coming to get you. Rape's coming to find you. Once it does, it will come back to remind you, it can visit you at any time and at any place. No matter how loud you scream or how hard you fight off; the pool of your tears crashing will drown out any sound of disobedience that'll give away rape's encounter. You're not alive yet living; you're not dead but willing.

Acknowledgement

Acknowledgement – to admit the existence or truth of something. Don't forget, nor necessarily forgive but remember. Forgetting is denial while acknowledgement is moving on. Acknowledgement signifies the power you hold – you know what happened to you, you remember what happened to you but you don't accept it. If you accept, you allow the next rapist to justify his/hers actions. Admittance is the pedestal for the next victim. Speaking out is the reminder that sexual assault is not okay. Reporting rape is the set up for the persecution of wrong doers. You may never be able to change what happened to you but you can alter what happens to the next vulnerable girl or boy. Acknowledgement isn't here to cradle and patronise you, it is here to empower you and take you on a journey that'll change your trauma into self-love. Acknowledgement is here to return the feelings of trust, respect and confidence back to you. You'll never get it all back but acknowledgment is here to rid the baggage of blame and replace it with the development of peace. Rape broke your bones, thieved your ability of choice but acknowledgement is here to carry you to a safe place to allow you to heal.

Statistics for rape are only increasing. Hidden statistics for rape are increasing even more. Voices speaking out on rape are yet decreasing. Rape has made women and men feel scared, feel like speaking about it is pointless, that they won't be believed, and even worse – blamed. Men are emasculated almost instantly for the slightest indication of abuse they faced. Our voices must not be silenced but echoed. Rape has sewn your lips together but acknowledgement is slowly plucking out the thread that keeps them shut. The more silence, the more victims and the more predators that escape detection.

Acknowledgement is here to take you from that dark place and show you the light, show you that you don't have to keep quiet and live with it, that you can make a change. Healing is unlimited, growth is unstoppable. You are rebuilding the foundation, once smashed to pieces and there's nothing more inspirational than an injured bird learning how to fly once again. Trying to speak about your experience can be painful. The words stuck in your throat, causing you to gag. Rape will make you feel sick to your stomach, heart race and legs shake. You can't forget but you can move on. The pain will be your lesson to teach those at risk of exploitation. Acknowledgement for you becomes acknowledgment for a wider problem. Rape should not become typical of all the messed up things that are expected to happen to a woman. Rape culture should not be laughed upon by the young boys of the next generation. Rape needs to become acknowledged as an unthinkable act that we as a community must limit. We must teach children the element of choice, respect towards the opposite gender and the irrelevance of stereotypes. You don't need to participate in sexual activity to be perceived as masculine or desirable. You don't need to inflict pain to be seen as tough. Acknowledgment must be feasted upon in order to spread awareness.

Rape no longer dictates you further, acknowledgment has stepped in to show you the world is yours to explore if you allow yourself to walk away from the self-pity inflicted by your captor. Acknowledgement is a process, and one for the better. You won't get the old you back but a new improved version. You can ponder in emotional distress or grab onto acknowledgement, and stand tall, head raised and spread the word. Rape is not okay. Rape is not acceptable. Rape does not need to become a part of who you are. Rape dragged you down into the devil's grasp, but you held on tight to all the hope you had left and persevered. All due to the support of acknowledgement. Acknowledgement is your friend not foe. You give your body away by choice, not force. With acknowledgement by your side, rape can't tell you what you already know. The difference is, rape will use your incident to trip you up at the slightest smell, sound, thought or touch of a man yet acknowledgement uses it to help give back your voice and speak out. Yes means yes, and no means no. I've had enough, I will speak out and call your bluff.

Chapter 10

Suicidal Thoughts

Suicidal thoughts – thoughts based around one wanting to inflict severe harm to injure or kill oneself. Every breath is unbearable and every morning is a challenge. Getting up, going to work or school feels like a death sentence – breathing this air is a death sentence. A death sentence you can't wait to reach. You want to let go of this thing you call life. You can't do it anymore. It's all too much. The pain can't taunt you if you're no longer there to suffer it. Cut yourself. Overdose. Drown. Just die. That's what your thoughts tell you. No one will miss you. All will forget about your painful existence.

What's life when you don't feel alive? What's death when you already feel dead? When your heart beats and yet your body remains lifeless. When you speak but the words are meaningless. Suicidal thoughts are here to tell you what you're not and what you won't ever be. It wants to save the world the trouble of another worthless human being. Because that's what you are, you're worthless; a burden. Every gasp of air feels like you're swallowing needles. Every tear burns your skin. Every step and movement, breaks you bit by bit. What's a life of dismay? You have nothing to live for but this cycle of emptiness. Suicidal thoughts nests its demons inside your head and finally they hatch. Bitch, slut, unloved, useless, weird or loner; all these terms fill up inside until you eventually just snap. All the concept of life does is add another scar to your arm. Add another referral to mental health. Add another failed suicide attempt. Why live when you have nothing to live for, just something to die for – peace.

You wake and cry. Roll over and try. But all you can do is reminisce/think about how you want to die. People care, God wants to repair you but even the devil himself is scared to take on someone as troubled as you. There's no one more ruthless than the one who lacks the capacity to feel. Suicidal thoughts remind you of your abnormalities, the things that make you stand out; it compiles these to tell you why you should exit your body and flee to your awaiting casket. The thoughts won't tell you anything good as they just belittle you and make you feel like there's no other option. Death is the only way out. It's the easier way out. Slit your wrists while you bath and all your problems will drown with you. You can't feel what's not there. If you're not here, how can you hurt about the way you feel. This world was not created for everybody, you're the anomaly that needs to be removed as you're an obstruction to those deserving of life.

You can't carry on as it's too much for you and so your journeys come to an end. Your mind has given up on hope and your heart is too broken up to heal; worst of all your lungs are restricting your ability to breath the poisonous air that forces you live this life. Finally your thoughts have dragged you to your senses as they've finally got you to fulfil your dream. Blood pours out, life bleeds away and your eyes are barely open. Suicidal thoughts have beaten you down and you've given up. You didn't live for yourself but you died believing that your decision was inevitable. Your soul already bruised can no longer pull you through. No more waking in the morning with that stabbing pain in your chest, a reminder that you will always feel like this. This time the knife cut too deep and resuscitation will make no difference. You can't resurrect what was already dead. You can't heal what was already broken. You can't cure the disease of suicidal thoughts this late on as each organ has become dysfunctional beyond repair. Roses are red, violets are blue, felt rejected by the world so suicide cradled you.

Survival

Survival – the state or fact of continuing to exist or live in spite of difficult circumstances.

The thoughts fade, the wounds heal – you survived. You survived the torment of suicidal thoughts, once hostage you are now free of your captor. Free of the pain, hurt and cycle of being unable to feel good enough. Survival has dug you out of your grave and given you a breath of life. A second chance to change your perspective on life – a chance to appreciate and not procrastinate in your life. Suicidal thoughts told you to die and slit your wrists but survival tells you that every second you breathe is worth it; you are more than you think. It bandaged your wrists and took away your blades; survival told you that you are better than this. You deserve more than this. Survival watched you come back to life and start again. It watched you pick yourself back up and tell suicidal thoughts, "no more". Suicidal thoughts drained your body of life, survival filled it with love, appreciation and worth.

Each day is a struggle, but you take it day by day. You wake in the morning and give yourself a routine in order to give your life some purpose. That's one thing suicidal thoughts can't take away. It stole your happiness as well as your will to live but it can't steal purposefulness. Purpose: The one thing that keeps you going, the thing that keeps you away from suicidal thoughts. Survival has stepped in, wooed you and made you feel worth it. Survival filled that empty void inside you and made you a fighter. You hang onto life with a firm grip, one so firm that suicidal thoughts can't manage to make you slip back. It tries to pull you down with thoughts of self-harm, anxiety and depression; but survival gives you content, pleasantness and progression to hold onto living and to pull yourself over the rails. Survival is a running tap that's here to overflow you with thoughts of what you can be and what you can achieve; not with the venomous dreams of suicidal thoughts, thoughts that want nothing but to see you perish.

Yet never be deceived by the form suicidal thoughts approach you in – the devil presented himself as a devoted friend before foe. These thoughts are never permanent even though they seem long-term. Everything seems to worsen day by day. Good things go away quicker than the bad things come. Pain lasts longer than happiness. The days seem longer and your heart feels weaker. Your body goes limp. Drained of love, comfort and joy. Friends leave while family disown. The bills get higher. You become empty inside. You're never good enough. Never wanted enough and never appreciated, respected or loved. No good has come. Not yet. And that's because things only get worse to get better.